SAY, DAD! WE'VE GOT A LITTLE PETITION GOING HERE!

YOUR COOKING HAS BEEN SO BAD LATELY THAT WE'VE DECIDED TO FILE AN OFFICIAL PROTEST AND DEMAND BETTER MEALS!

ELLEN AND I HAVE ALREADY SIGNED IT! NOW WE NEED **YOUR** SIGNATURE!

YOU WANT ME TO SIGN A PETITION AGAINST **MYSELF**?

SURE! MAKE IT UNANIMOUS, AND WE'LL ALL GO OUT FOR PIZZA!

SO LET ME GET THIS STRAIGHT.... YOU'RE TIRED OF MY COOKING SO YOU'VE WRITTEN THIS PETITION TO PROTEST.

CHECK!

WE'RE TIRED OF EATING THE SAME MEALS WEEK AFTER WEEK! WE'RE SICK OF LEFTOVERS! WE'RE NOT GOING TO **TAKE** IT ANYMORE!

WE DEMAND A CHANGE!

VEEEEEERY FUNNY.

THAT'S THE THIRD TIME THIS WEEK WE'VE GOTTEN DETENTION!

I **SAID** I WAS SORRY!

SORRY'S NOT GOOD ENOUGH, NATE! I'M **SICK** OF GETTING INTO TROUBLE ALL THE TIME BECAUSE OF YOU!

I'M OFFICIALLY GIVING YOU THE "SILENT TREATMENT".

THE "SILENT TREATMENT"?

STARTIIIINNG.... **NOW!**

NO! WAIT! YOU HAVE TO SHOW ME HOW TO DO THE MATH HOME- WORK FIRST!

8

....SO THEN FRANCIS GOT ALL BENT OUT OF SHAPE AND DECIDED TO GIVE ME THE "SILENT TREATMENT"! REAL MATURE, RIGHT?

MR. ROSA

AND THEN AFTER A WHILE, I THOUGHT: WAIT A MINUTE! WHY AM **I** THE ONLY ONE GETTING THE "SILENT TREATMENT"? WHY SHOULDN'T I GIVE **FRANCIS** THE "SILENT TREATMENT"?

MR. ROSA

THAT MAKES SENSE, DON'T YOU THINK? **I** THINK IT MAKES SENSE! SO NOW NEITHER ONE OF US IS SPEAKING! WE'RE GIVING EACH OTHER THE "SILENT TREATMENT"!

MR. ROSA

WHY DOESN'T ANYBODY EVER GIVE **ME** THE "SILENT TREATMENT"?

MR. ROSA

Peirce

TELL NATE THAT DUMPING HIM AS MY BEST FRIEND WAS THE SMARTEST THING I EVER DID!

TELL FRANCIS THAT HE'S NEVER DONE **ANYTHING** SMART, AND THAT HE'LL NEVER FIND ANOTHER FRIEND LIKE ME!

TELL NATE THAT I DON'T **WANT** ANOTHER FRIEND LIKE HIM, AND THAT I'M SORRY I EVER **MET** HIM!

TELL FRANCIS THAT...

LOOK, IS THIS GOING TO TAKE MUCH LONGER? I HAVE BAND PRACTICE.

THERE'S FRANCIS.

I WONDER IF HE'S STILL MAD AT ME....

AT THIS POINT I CAN'T EVEN REMEMBER WHAT WE'RE FIGHTING ABOUT.

WELL, HERE GOES NOTHING.

HI, FRANCIS.

OH.... HI.

UH... WANT SOME OF MY SODA?

SURE!

WANT SOME OF MY JUICE?

THANKS!

CHEERS!

CHEERS!

IT'S EASIER TO SWALLOW YOUR PRIDE IF YOU HAVE SOMETHING TO WASH IT DOWN WITH!

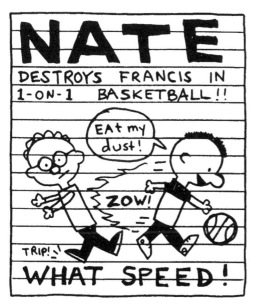

attention ART LOVERS!!

★ ★ ★ ★ ★ ★ ★ ★ ★

It's the

RUSTY SIENNA
FAN CLUB
NEWSLETTER!

"Let's Paint"
(our motto)

Written & Illustrated by:
NATE WRIGHT

(1)

Fans, even a chimp knows that Rusty Sienna is the world's most successful artist, and star of his own TV show, "Oil Painting With Rusty."

our hero ←

But **REAL** fans of Rusty want to know **MORE**!

(2)

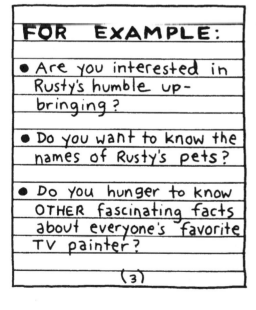

FOR EXAMPLE:

● Are you interested in Rusty's humble up-bringing?

● Do you want to know the names of Rusty's pets?

● Do you hunger to know OTHER fascinating facts about everyone's favorite TV painter?

(3)

NOT REALLY.

HERE'S THE NEXT SIX PAGES!

WHO'S THAT A PICTURE OF, MRS. GODFREY?

THAT'S MY HUSBAND.

THEN WHY IS HE SMILING?

WAP!

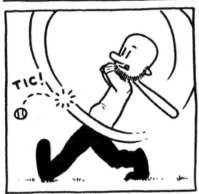

BASEBALL UPDATE!

Sports fans, it's Little League season again, and **JOE'S PIZZA** is hoping to improve on last year's record!

JOE'S PIZZA is led by the multi-talented _Nate Wright_, a sure-fire league All Star. Other teams around the league are quaking at the thought of facing the "NATE JUGGERNAUT."

KRAK!

He pitches! He catches! He hits! He runs! Whatever the team needs, Nate is there! He DOES IT ALL!

WRIGHT! HURRY UP WITH THAT WATER JUG!

OKAY, COACH.

ANOTHER YEAR OF PLAYING FOR "JOE'S PIZZA".

IT'S SUCH A JOKE.

ALL THE OTHER TEAMS ARE LAUGHING AT US BECAUSE WE'RE CALLED "JOE'S PIZZA"! WE'VE GOT TO DO SOMETHING TO CHANGE OUR IMAGE!

I KNOW WHAT WE NEED! WE NEED A MASCOT!

LIKE WHAT? A GIANT ANCHOVY?

NO, NO, SOMETHING **CLASSY!** A GUY IN A CHICKEN SUIT!

WHAT'S THAT?

IT'S A STAT SHEET! I'M COMPILING A LIST OF STATISTICS FOR ALL THE PLAYERS ON OUR TEAM!

FOR EXAMPLE.... SO FAR THIS SEASON, YOU HAVE A BATTING AVERAGE OF .000.

I'VE ONLY BEEN UP **ONE TIME!**

YOU'RE ON A PACE TO MATCH YOUR AVERAGE FROM **LAST** SEASON!

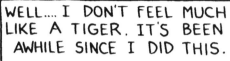

TEDDY MERTZ WAS VOTED "CLASS COMEDIAN"!

WHAT?

TEDDY MERTZ? HE'S NOT FUNNY! HE'S NEVER DONE ANYTHING FUNNY IN HIS **LIFE!**

NAME **ONE** TIME TEDDY MERTZ HAS DONE SOMETHING FUNNY! JUST **ONE TIME!**

WHAT ABOUT THAT WEDGIE HE GAVE YOU DURING CO-ED VOLLEYBALL?

YOU JUST CAN'T LET ME FORGET THAT, CAN YOU?

It started last September.
We shuffled back to school
With cruel teachers, tiny desks,
And lots of stupid rules.

We tried to pay attention
Although we felt quite bored.
We did our best when given tests
And "F's" were our reward!

But now our suffering is through.
Let's raise a happy cheer.
The school year's past
We're free at last.
And SUMMERTIME IS HERE!

BOY, SOME OF THESE PARENTS TAKE THEIR LITTLE LEAGUE BASEBALL A BIT TOO SERIOUSLY!

LOOK AT THEM! SHOUTING AT THEIR CHILDREN..... SCREAMING AT THE UMPIRE.....

DON'T THEY REALIZE THIS GAME IS FOR THE **KIDS'** ENJOYMENT?

BY CALLING ATTENTION TO THEMSELVES, THEY ONLY EMBARRASS THEIR CHILDREN! I'M NOT GOING TO DO THAT!

IT'S ONLY A GAME! I'M NOT GOING TO TURN IT INTO SOME BIG EVENT!

HEADS UP!

HUH?

BONK!

WH.... WHAT HAPPENED?

DAD, WHY CAN'T YOU PAY ATTENTION TO THE GAME LIKE THE OTHER PARENTS?

♡ EVERLOVIN'

ELLEN!

The life and loves of a clueless high school sophomore!

As our story opens, Ellen has just said goodbye for the summer to her boyfriend Kenny!

Goodbye my love!

Chow, mein!

While Kenny is off at his family's cottage on the Maine coast, Ellen is pining away at home!!

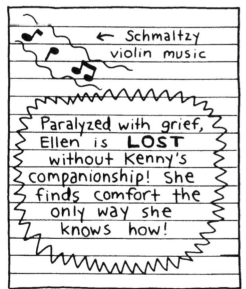

← Schmaltzy violin music

Paralyzed with grief, Ellen is **LOST** without Kenny's companionship! She finds comfort the only way she knows how!

YOU ATE **ALL** THE COOKIES?

(BURP.)

SIGH..... NO LETTER FROM KENNY.

OOOOOOH! TROUBLE IN PARADISE?

NO, THERE'S NOT "TROUBLE IN PARADISE," YOU LITTLE JERK!

OH YEAH? HOW MANY LETTERS HAS HE WRITTEN YOU?

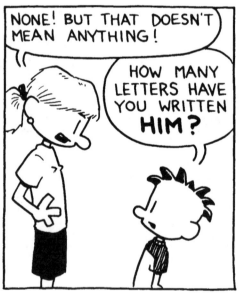

NONE! BUT THAT DOESN'T MEAN ANYTHING!

HOW MANY LETTERS HAVE YOU WRITTEN **HIM**?

NINETEEN.

UH-OH! ALL ABOARD THE "DUMPS-VILLE EXPRESS"!

OKAY, ELLEN, YOU CAN STOP MOPING. YOU GOT A LETTER FROM KENNY.

I DID?

YUP. HE'S DOING FINE. HE GOT A JOB WORKING IN A DINER.

HE JOINED A SOFTBALL LEAGUE, BUT THEY HAVEN'T HAD ANY GAMES YET. OH, AND HE GOT POISON IVY WHILE MOWING THE LAWN.

GIVE ME THAT!

THEN ON THE SECOND PAGE, HE STARTS GETTING MUSHY...

4TH OF JULY
★ FAIR! ★

This is the best part of the summer. A big fair comes to town for the 4th of July. There are games, rides, and all sorts of cool stuff.

Every year the fair gets bigger and better. But it will have to go a long way to be better than last year.

YA-HOO!

Last year I won a prize at the ring toss. Last year they had the most awesome fireworks. Last year was a total blast!

LAST YEAR, YOU GOT SICK ON THE TILT-A-WHIRL!

I KNOW. REMIND ME TO AVOID THOSE CORN DOGS.

IT TOOK ME TWENTY-EIGHT TRIES, BUT I FINALLY WON A PRIZE AT THE RING TOSS!

SEE? I WON A LITTLE PLASTIC CHANGE PURSE! NOW I HAVE A PLACE TO KEEP ALL MY MONEY!

THAT'S FUNNY...

TWENTY-EIGHT TRIES, YOU SAY?

ENJOY THE FAIR, BOYS.

MAN! RUNNING INTO MRS. GODFREY AT THE FAIR! HOW WEIRD CAN YOU GET?

I KNOW!

I WONDER WHAT SHE'S DOING HERE...

MOONLIGHTING IN THE "HALL OF ODDITIES"?

SAAAY! I **DID** SEE A SIGN READING "MISSING LINK WOMAN"!

OOOOH! DADDY! YOU GOT **SUNBURNED!**

I KNOW...

I WAS WORKING IN THE GARDEN AND I DIDN'T REALIZE HOW STRONG THE SUN WAS.

THAT LOOKS BAD! YOU SHOULD GO SEE A DOCTOR!

MAYBE I WILL...

Peirce

DR. CESSPOOL'S **SUNBURN CITY!**

Here comes another one! And boy, is he FRIED!

By golly, I LOVE this time of year!

THE MAN'S MADE OF STONE.

I NEVER HAVE ANY MONEY.

WELL, THERE ARE LOTS OF WAYS YOU COULD EARN SOME.....

HOW ABOUT COLLECTING EMPTY CANS AND BOTTLES? YOU CAN TURN THEM IN FOR THE DEPOSIT!

CANS AND BOTTLES! GREAT IDEA, DAD!

GLUG GLUG GLUG GLUG GLUG

Nate Wright
DIRECTOR!

I just saw a documentary on T.V., and it gave me the most awesome idea. I am going to film my **OWN** documentary!

QUIET ON THE SET!

I am going to call it "A DAY IN THE LIFE OF THE WRIGHT FAMILY." I will use Dad's camcorder to record events around the house.

TRA LA DE DA ♪

I can edit this out later.

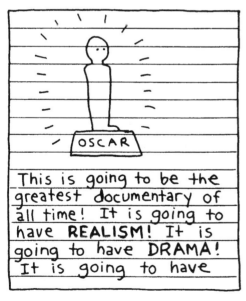

OSCAR

This is going to be the greatest documentary of all time! It is going to have **REALISM**! It is going to have **DRAMA**! It is going to have

ACTION!

HUH?

YOU'RE GOING TO DO WHAT?

I'M GOING TO MAKE A DOCUMENTARY ABOUT OUR FAMILY!

I'LL BE FILMING EVERY-DAY EVENTS AROUND THE HOUSE, THEN WEAVING THEM INTO A SEAMLESS NARRATIVE!

SEE THE BERET? SEE THE SUNGLASSES? THAT MEANS I'M THE DIRECTOR! I'M IN CHARGE! YOU HAVE TO DO WHAT **I** SAY!

SOUNDS LIKE FUN.

WORK WITH ME, PEOPLE, **WORK** WITH ME!

CLAP CLAP CLAP

OKAY, DAD, THIS IS GOING TO BE THE FIRST SCENE IN MY FILM!

YOU JUST SIT THERE AND DRINK YOUR COFFEE LIKE YOU DO EVERY MORNING!

OKAY.

WAIT, WAIT! HOLD IT! CUT!

WAS I DOING SOMETHING WRONG?

SORT OF. I'M GETTING **WAY** TOO MUCH GLARE OFF YOUR HEAD!

I'M FILMING ANOTHER SCENE FOR MY DOCUMENTARY, ELLEN!

NOT NOW, NATE! I'M ON THE PHONE!

THAT'S OKAY! YOU WON'T EVEN NOTICE ME!

YES I **WILL!** NOW BEAT IT! THIS IS A PRIVATE CONVERSATION!

OOOOOOH! REALISTIC DIALOGUE! THAT'LL BE A NICE TOUCH!

NATE, GET OUT OF HERE! NOW!

EASY ON THE CLOSE-UPS, ELLEN! YOU'RE FOGGING UP MY LENS!

SHARON, CAN I CALL YOU BACK?

SHICK!
SHICK!
SHUCK!

OW!

WOW! THAT WAS **GREAT!** DAD CUTS HIMSELF SHAVING! GRITTY REALISM! AND I CAPTURED IT ALL ON TAPE!

WHOOPS. NO, I DIDN'T. I FORGOT TO TURN THE CAMERA ON. **DANG!**

SAY, DO YOU THINK YOU COULD...?

NO!

IT'S TIME FOR ANOTHER EDITION OF "BIG NATE'S BASEBALL NEWSLETTER"!

Hello again, sports fans! The Little League baseball season is winding down, and JOE'S PIZZA is roaring toward the playoffs!

JOE'S PIZZA

Not much was expected of JOE'S PIZZA during spring training, but they have proven the 'experts' wrong by compiling an 8-5 record!

TOTAL WHIFF!

Hapless opponent

"WHAT is behind this surprising surge?" you may ask.

What is behind this surprising surge?

Clearly the team owes much of its success to the scintillating play of **NATE WRIGHT**, a likely league all-star!

What a SNAG!

Thunderous ovation

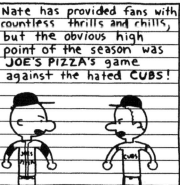

Nate has provided fans with countless thrills and chills, but the obvious high point of the season was JOE'S PIZZA's game against the hated CUBS!

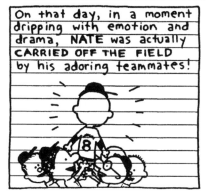

On that day, in a moment dripping with emotion and drama, NATE was actually CARRIED OFF THE FIELD by his adoring teammates!

OF COURSE, YOU **WERE** UNCONSCIOUS AT THE TIME!

I WAS ONLY **DAZED!** THE BALL DIDN'T HIT ME **THAT** HARD!

AT THE MALL!

Definitely one of the funnest things to do during summer vacation is to go hang out at the mall.

A lot of times you run into people you know, which can be cool. And also, the whole mall is air-conditioned, which is totally key.

But the best thing about the mall is that it is FREE. You can just browse around the stores all day and it doesn't cost you anything!

LET ME GET THIS STRAIGHT.... YOU GO INTO A STORE AND ACCIDENTALLY BREAK THIS CERAMIC MONKEY.....

RIGHT!....

THE STORE MANAGER MAKES YOU **BUY** THE THING....

RIGHT!

....AND NOW YOU'RE GOING TO GLUE IT BACK TOGETHER AND GIVE IT TO YOUR SISTER AS A **BIRTH-DAY PRESENT?**

HEY, IT'S NOT THE GREATEST GIFT, BUT IT'S THE **THOUGHT** THAT COUNTS!

MY POINT EXACTLY.

OF COURSE, EIGHTY-NINE CENTS **IS** A LITTLE MORE THAN I HAD PLANNED TO SPEND....

CAMPING OUT!

Francis is coming over tonight to sleep over. We are going to have a camp-out!

Dad said we could pitch our tent out in the backyard. While everybody else is cooped up inside, Francis and I will be <u>outside</u>! While everybody else is in their beds, we will be in sleeping bags!

This is going to be so wicked. We are really going to be roughing it. Francis and I are going to be real outdoorsmen!

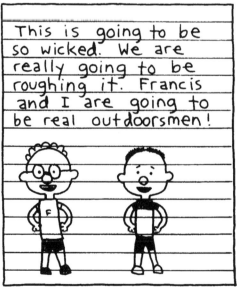

DO YOU THINK IT TAKES REAL OUTDOORSMEN TWO HOURS TO PITCH A TENT?

OH, **GREAT!** THE DUMB EXTENSION CORD DOESN'T REACH OUT HERE!

LOOK AT NATE AND FRANCIS, "CAMPING OUT" IN THE BACKYARD!

I GUESS THEY'RE STILL AWAKE..... I CAN HEAR THEIR VOICES.

THEY'RE PROBABLY TELLING HORROR STORIES, TRYING TO SCARE EACH OTHER SILLY!

SCHOOL STARTS IN FIVE WEEKS.

NYAA!

Summer

FASHION REPORT!

Hello again, fashion mavens! Out on the runway, our model ELLEN WRIGHT is showing off the hottest outfit in the fashion world today!

VOGUE   COSMO   WILDLIFE TODAY

Note the sleek polyester slacks.... the stylish vest..... the classic bow tie.... and topping it all off, the jaunty hat!

TA-DA!

Yes, Ellen is ready for action in this sporty ensemble! It is the perfect outfit for the woman who is GOING PLACES!

SIGH....

WELCOME TO DILLY BURGER

EMPLOYEE ENTRANCE

FRANCIS, I JUST CAN'T FIGURE OUT WHY YOU'RE SO CRAZY ABOUT MY SISTER!

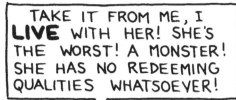

TAKE IT FROM ME, I **LIVE** WITH HER! SHE'S THE WORST! A MONSTER! SHE HAS NO REDEEMING QUALITIES WHATSOEVER!

HERE, GUYS.... A COUPLE OF DELUXE BURGERS ON THE HOUSE.

OKAY, SO SHE HAS HER MOMENTS.

SIGH....

WELCOME TO THE FIRST ANNUAL "NATE WRIGHT COOKOUT," FRANCIS!

WHAT'LL IT BE, A HOT DOG OR A HAMBURGER?

A HOT DOG!

YOU KNOW, I **KNEW** YOU'D SAY THAT!

I SHOULD HAVE KNOWN THAT **YOU**, OF ALL PEOPLE, WOULD PREFER A HOT DOG!

WHY'S THAT?

BECAUSE YOU'RE SUCH A **WEENIE!**

WA HA HA HA! OH HO HO!

FRANCIS WENT HOME?

SOME PEOPLE HAVE NO SENSE OF HUMOR. HERE, HELP ME WASH THE MUSTARD OUT OF MY HAIR.

I'VE COME UP WITH YET ANOTHER BRILLIANT IDEA, FRANCIS! I'M GOING TO BECOME A PSYCHOLOGIST!

CHECK IT OUT! INK BLOTS! I MADE THEM MYSELF! AM I AUTHENTIC OR **WHAT?**

YOU CAN BE MY FIRST PATIENT, FRANCIS! TELL ME WHAT YOU SEE!

A TOTAL LOSER.

HUH? WHERE? ALL I SEE IS A GIANT SPIDER!

OKAY, FRANCIS, I'M GOING TO GIVE YOU MY "INK BLOT TEST"!

JUST TELL ME WHAT YOU SEE.... AND REMEMBER, THERE ARE NO RIGHT OR WRONG ANSWERS!

OKAY.... I SEE A SAIL-BOAT.

NOPE. SORRY.

I THOUGHT THERE WERE NO RIGHT OR WRONG ANSWERS!

I JUST SAID THAT TO EARN YOUR TRUST. NO, YOU WERE **WAY** OFF.

I'M DRAWING A COMIC STRIP ABOUT WHAT IT WOULD BE LIKE TO HAVE OUR OWN TV SHOW!

I'LL BE THE STAR, SEE, AND YOU'LL BE MY JOVIAL SIDEKICK!

JOVIAL SIDEKICK?

IT'S AN EASY JOB. ALL YOU HAVE TO DO IS LAUGH AT MY JOKES.

YOU CALL THAT EASY?

DID I MENTION THAT I CAN REPLACE YOU AT ANY TIME?

HOW COME WHENEVER WE DO SOMETHING, **YOU** HAVE TO BE IN CHARGE?

VERY SIMPLE, FRANCIS!

THERE ARE LEADERS AND THERE ARE FOLLOWERS! **I'M** A LEADER! I'M A TAKE-CHARGE PERSON! I LIKE TO RUN THINGS!

WHEN YOU'RE A TAKE-CHARGE PERSON LIKE ME, YOU WELCOME RESPONSIBILITY! IN FACT, YOU **CRAVE** RESPONSIBILITY!

NATE! I THOUGHT I TOLD YOU TO MOW THE LAWN!

WHOOPS. QUICK, LET'S SNEAK OUT THE BACK.

NATE WRIGHT, MASTER CARTOONIST, IS AT IT AGAIN!

CHECK IT OUT! I'M DRAWING A COMIC ABOUT THE TWO OF US!

"THE ADVENTURES OF NATE AND HIS BESPECKLED PAL, FRANCIS."

YOU DON'T MEAN "BESPECKLED"! YOU MEAN "BESPECTACLED"! THAT MEANS I WEAR GLASSES!

"BESPECKLED," ON THE OTHER HAND, MEANS "COVERED WITH SPOTS"!

YOU USED THE WRONG WORD!

OKAY, MR. KNOW-IT-ALL! CALM DOWN! I'LL MAKE IT RIGHT!

DOT DOT DOT
DOT DOT
DOT DOT DOT
DOT DOT
DOT DOT
DOT
DOT
DOT
DOT
DOT
DOT
DOT

Beat the HEAT!

It's a searing hot day as our heroes, NATE and FRANCIS, set out on an epic journey across the unforgiving desert!

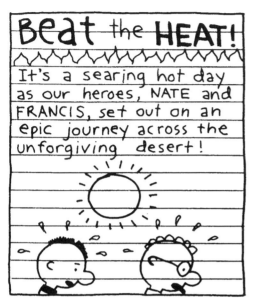

The sun pounds down relentlessly on our two travelers as they drag themselves across the white-hot sand! They CAN'T HOLD OUT MUCH LONGER!

GASP!

WATER!

But **WAIT!**
Finally, their quest is over! At long last, Nate and Francis reach their destination!

HERE'S A GOOD SPOT!

HOLD IT. DON'T WE WANT TO BE CLOSER TO THE SNACK BAR?

Nate Wright's BEACH TIPS!

Hey, studs-in-training!! The seashore is not only a great place to work on your tan, it's the ideal spot to meet girls!

SURF'S UP!

If you're lucky, you may find yourself soaking up rays right next to a meeting of "BABES UNLIMITED"!

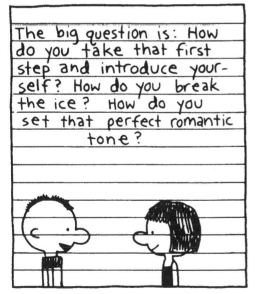

The big question is: How do you take that first step and introduce yourself? How do you break the ice? How do you set that perfect romantic tone?

CARE FOR A "CHEEZ DOODLE"?

I THOUGHT TODAY WAS GOING TO BE ONE OF THE HAPPIEST DAYS OF MY LIFE!

I THOUGHT KENNY WOULD FINALLY COME BACK FROM VACATION, AND THAT HE'D TELL ME HOW MUCH HE MISSED ME, AND IT WOULD BE SO BEAUTIFUL!

INSTEAD, I'M SITTING HERE WAITING FOR HIM TO COME OVER AND BREAK UP WITH ME, SHATTERING MY HEART INTO A MILLION PIECES!

MY LIFE STINKS.

HEY, ELLEN! WHEN KENNY DUMPS YOU, CAN I WATCH?

OMIGOSH! IT'S KENNY! HE'S WALKING UP THE DRIVEWAY!

WELL, IF HE WANTS TO BREAK UP WITH ME, LET HIM DO IT! IT'S **HIS** LOSS!

I WON'T GIVE HIM THE SATISFACTION OF KNOWING HE'S HURT ME! I'M NOT GOING TO CRY! I'M NOT GOING TO BEG!

HI!

PLEASE DON'T BREAK UP WITH ME.

WHAT'S ALL THIS ABOUT BREAK- ING UP?

WELL... IT'S THAT LAST CARD YOU SENT.

WHEN YOU SIGNED IT "TAKE CARE", I THOUGHT IT MEANT YOU DIDN'T WANT TO GO OUT WITH ME ANYMORE!

OH, **THAT!**

I ONLY SIGNED IT THAT WAY BECAUSE IT WAS A **POST- CARD!** I DIDN'T WANT TO WRITE ALL SORTS OF MUSHY STUFF THAT ANY- BODY COULD READ!

OH, KENNY....

HI, KIDS! HOW GOES THE DUMP- FEST?

Big Nate is distributed internationally by Universal Uclick.

The Complete Big Nate Volume 2 copyright © 2016 by United Feature Syndicate, Inc. All rights reserved. Printed in China. No part of this book may be used or reproduced in any manner whatsoever without written permission except in the case of reprints in the context of reviews.

Andrews McMeel Publishing
a division of Andrews McMeel Universal
1130 Walnut Street, Kansas City, Missouri 64106

www.andrewsmcmeel.com

16 17 18 19 20 SDB 10 9 8 7 6 5 4 3 2 1

ISBN: 978-1-4494-8201-5

These strips appeared in newspapers from
May 7, 1992, through September 5, 1992.

Big Nate can be viewed on the Internet at
www.gocomics.com/big_nate

Attention: Schools and Businesses
Andrews McMeel books are available at quantity discounts with bulk purchase for educational, business, or sales promotional use. For information, please e-mail the Andrews McMeel Publishing Special Sales Department: specialsales@amuniversal.com.

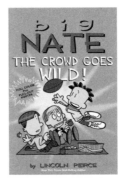

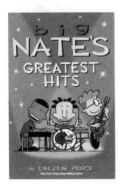